World Gospel Hymns

für gemischten Chor (SATB)
mit Klavierbegleitung
for Mixed Choir (SATB)
and Piano Accompaniment

Herausgegeben von
Edited by
Jochen Rieger

ED 22092
ISMN 979-0-001-20117-9
ISBN 978-3-7957-4941-5

www.schott-music.com

Mainz · London · Berlin · Madrid · New York · Paris · Prague · Tokyo · Toronto
© 2015 SCHOTT MUSIC GmbH & Co. KG, Mainz · Printed in Germany

Die CD zum Buch:

Jochen Rieger (Produzent)
World Gospel Hymns
CD
Nr. 097.327, €D 14,95*
€A 15,30*/CHF 24.50* | SCM Hänssler

Release: März 2015

Impressum:

Bestellnummer: ED 22092
ISMN 979-0-001-20117-9
ISBN 978-3-7957-4941-5
Produktmanager: Cristian Maria Schempershofe Papen
Lektorat: Julia Gerber / Pascal Martiné
Grafik: Knut Schötteldreier, Köln

Titelfoto: © Ssirus W. Pakzad
© 2015 SCHOTT MUSIC GmbH & Co. KG, Mainz
Printed in Germany · BSS 56672

Vorwort

Geistliche Hymnen sind Schwergewichte vielgesungener geistlicher Lieder, die sich für Konzerte sowie auch für viele feierliche Anlässe wie Hochzeiten, Trauungen, Geburtstage, Gottesdienste, Beerdigungen, Amtseinführungen etc. hervorragend eignen. Es sind bewährte und von begnadeten Textern und Komponisten verfasste, durchlebte Zeugnisse und Vermächtnisse, die in das Repertoire eines jeden Chores und einer jeden zeitgemäßen Kantorei passen. Manche „Hymnen" sind als Choräle bekannt und werden weltweit gesungen, denn ihre Inhalte und Melodien haben bereits viele Generationen teilweise über Jahrhunderte innerlich berührt, begeistert und getröstet. Sie werden vermutlich auch uns und wohl die meisten aktuellen Songs überleben.

Daher verdienen sie angemessen respektvoll interpretiert, aber auch zeitgemäß arrangiert und instrumentiert zu werden, um von möglichst vielen Zuhörern erneut geschätzt und angenommen zu werden. Diese Arrangements können sowohl a cappella als auch mit aktueller Bandbesetzung (Schlagzeug, Bass, Gitarre, Piano etc.) vorgetragen werden. Und es ist immer wieder für alle begeisternd, wenn auch das Publikum mitmacht, weil die eine oder andere Melodie bekannt ist. Ich wünsche Ihnen viel Freude und Fantasie beim Singen.

Ihr
Jochen Rieger

Preface

These hymns are heavyweights among well-known religious songs, ideally suited for concert performance as well as for many solemn occasions such as wedding ceremonies, marriages, birthdays, church services, funerals, inaugurations and so on. Here are tried and trusted works, fruits of the experience of exceptionally gifted authors and composers, suitable for the repertoire of any choral group and any church choir. Many of these hymns are known as chorales and sung all over the world, for their content and melodies have already touched, inspired and comforted many generations, sometimes over centuries. They will probably outlive us and most of our popular songs, too.

They therefore deserve to be performed with appropriate respect – and with contemporary arrangements and instrumentation, in order to be appreciated and enjoyed by as many people as possible. These arrangements may either be performed a cappella or accompanied with modern band instruments (drums, bass, guitar, piano etc.) – and it is always encouraging when the audience or congregation joins in because they know one or other of the tunes.

I wish you great enjoyment and inspiration from your singing.

Best wishes,
Jochen Rieger
Translation: Julia Rushworth

Inhaltsverzeichnis

1. Amazing Grace

Melodie: American Traditional (um 1831)
Text: John Newton (1725–1807)
Satz: Jochen Rieger (*1956)

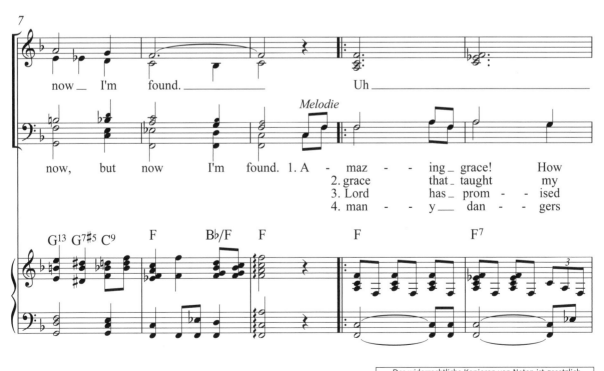

56 672

6

56 672

*) Textverteilung Altstimme

2. Rock Of Ages

Melodie: Thomas Hastings (1784–1872)
Text: Augustus M. Toplady (1740–1778)
Satz: Jochen Rieger (*1956)

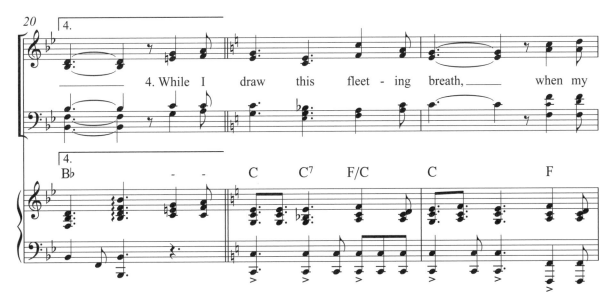

12

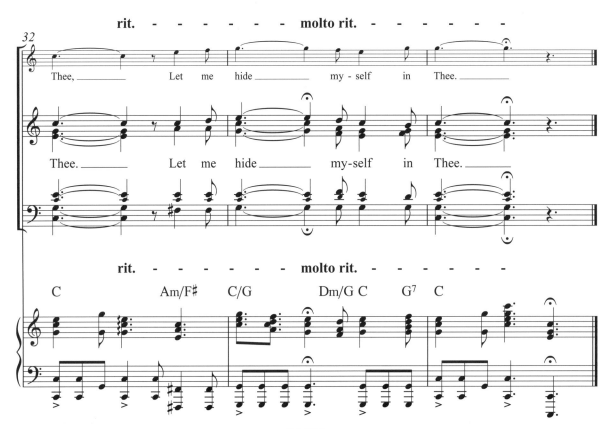

56 672

3. God Of Wonders

Melodie: Marc Byrd (*1970) & Steve Hindalong (*1959)
Text: Marc Byrd & Steve Hindalong
Satz: Jochen Rieger (*1956)

the heav - ens are Your tab - er - na - cle;_____
And as I stum - ble in the dark - ness_____

glo - ry to the Lord on_____ high._____
I will call Your name by_____ night._____

glo - - - ry to the Lord on_____ high._____
I will call Your name by_____ night._____

God of won - ders be - yond our gal - ax - y._____ You are

You are

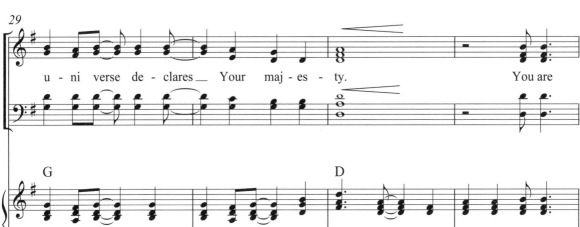

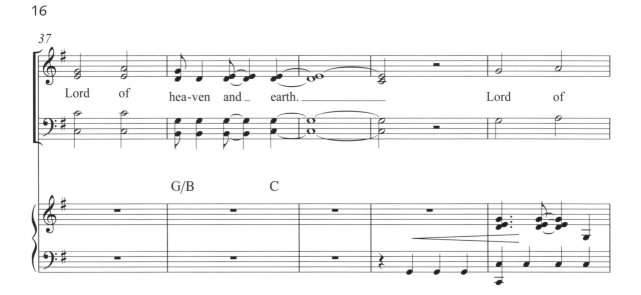

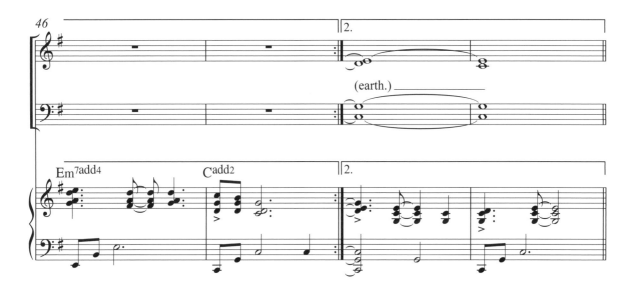

4. He's Got The Whole World

Melodie: Traditional Spiritual
Text: Traditional Spiritual
Satz: Jochen Rieger (*1956)

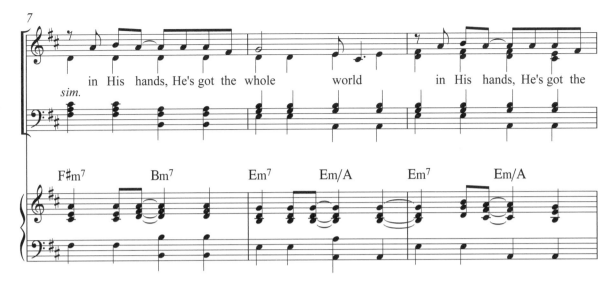

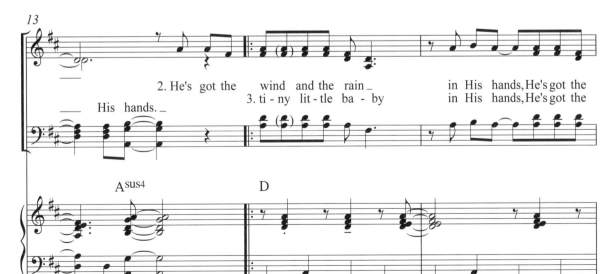

22

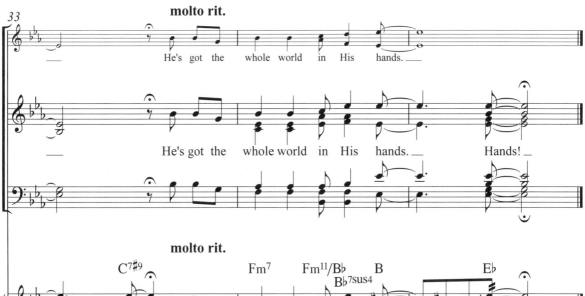

56 672

5. Great Is Thy Faithfulness

Bleibend ist deine Treu

Melodie: William M. Runyan (1870–1957)
Text: Thomas O. Chrisholm (1866–1960)
Satz: Jochen Rieger (*1956)

56 672

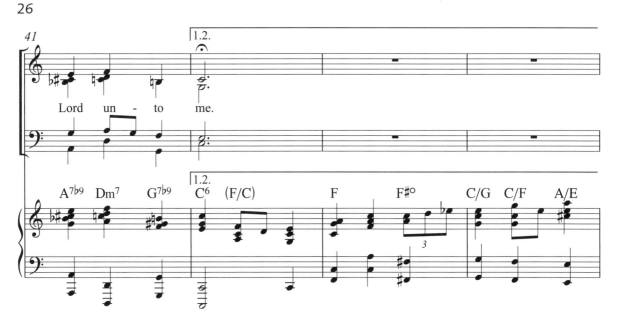

Lord un - to me.

me, n'to me. Great is Thy

faith - ful - ness, ___ Lord, un - to me.

6. Nobody Knows

Melodie: Amerikanisches Traditional
Text: Amerikanisches Traditional
Satz: Jochen Rieger (*1956)

56 672

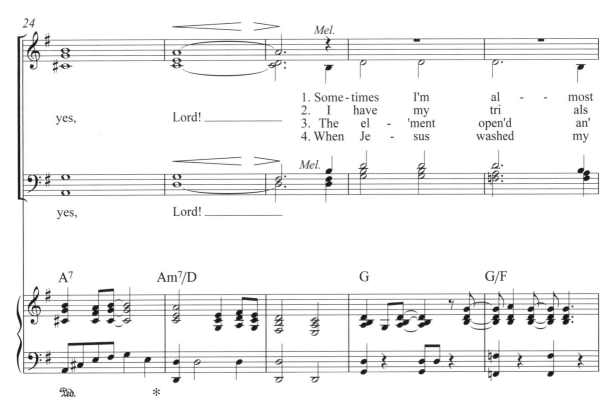

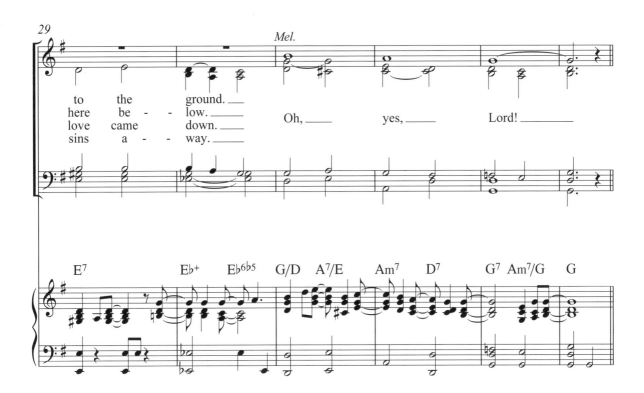

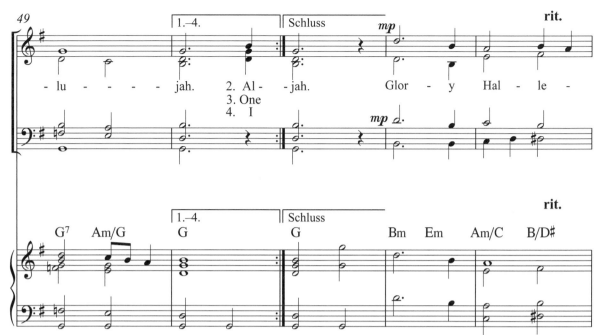

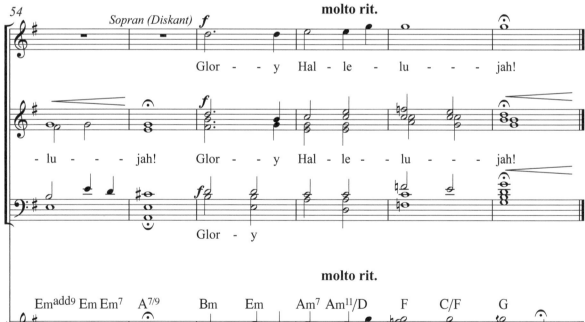

7. How Great Is Our God

Melodie: Chris Tomlin (*1972),
Jesse Reeves (*1975), Ed Cash (*1971)
Text: Chris Tomlin, Jesse Reeves, Ed Cash
Satz: Jochen Rieger (*1956)

nach Wdh. folgt:
D.S. al Coda

heart will sing: How great __ is our God! __ (How great)

nach Wdh. folgt:
D.S. al Coda

Coda ritard.

How great, __ how great __ is our God! __ How great,

how great __ is our God! __

Ablaufvorschlag: Intro-A-B-A2-B-CC-BB-Coda

8. Praise To The Lord, The Almighty

Melodie: Stralsund 1665
Text: Joachim Neander (1650–1680)
Engl. Übersetzung: Catherine Winkworth (1827–1878)
Satz: Jochen Rieger (*1956)

56 672

O my soul, praise Him, for He is thy health and sal - va - -
shel - ters thee un - der His wings, yes, so gen - tly sus - tain - - -
Sure - ly His good - ness and mer - cy here dai - ly at - tend ____
All that hath life and breath, come now with prais - es be - fore ____

Em⁷ D G B/D♯ Em Bm C G/B C B/D♯ Em Am D⁷

- tion! All ye who hear, now to His tem - ple ____ draw
- eth! Hast thou not seen how all thy long - ings have
thee. Pon - der a - new what the Al - might - y ____ can ____
Him. Let the A - men sound from His peo - ple ____ a -

G D⁷/A G/B C G C/E D G/B C Am⁷

Lyrics:

near; ___ Join me in glad ad - o - ra - - - - tion!
been ___ grant - ed in what He or - dain - - - eth?
do, ___ if with His love He be - friend _____ thee.
- gain: ___ glad - ly for aye we a - dore _____ Him.

Praise the Al - might - y! Praise the Al - might - y! Uh _____
Praise Him! Praise Him!

(Uh) _____

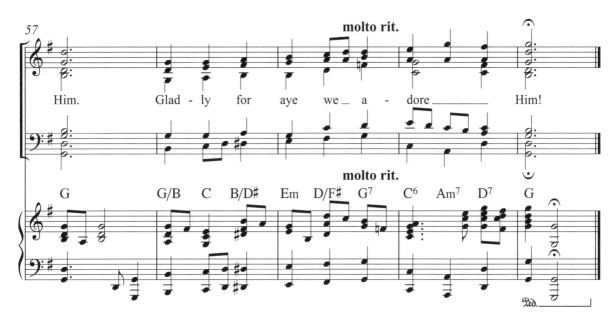

9. I Will Follow Him

Melodie: Frank Pourcel (1913–2000) / Paul Mauriat (1925–2006)
Text: Jacques Plante (1929–1986) / Arthur Altmann (1910–1994) / Norman Gimbel (*1927)
Satz: Jochen Rieger (*1956)

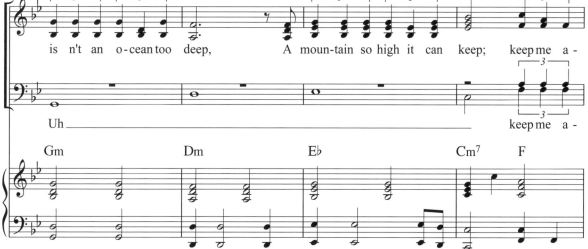

42

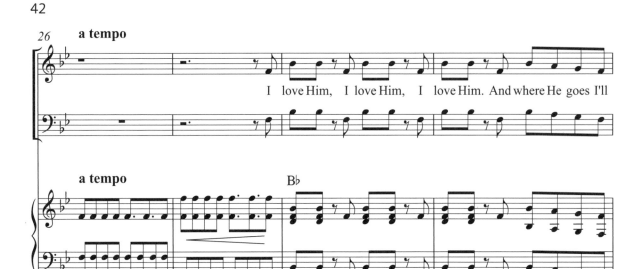

56 672

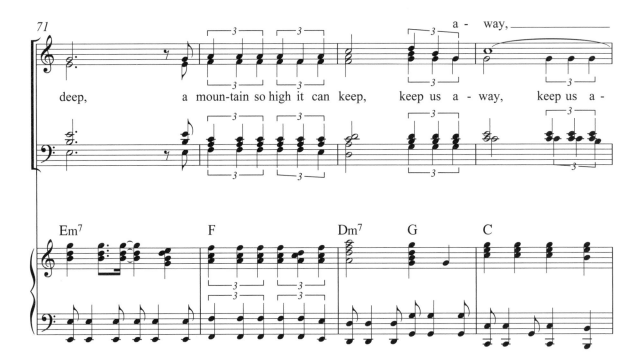

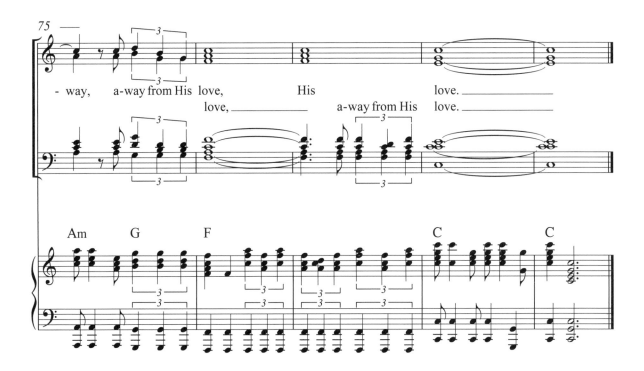

10. Sometimes I Feel

Melodie: Traditional
Text: Traditional
Satz: Jochen Rieger (*1956)

48

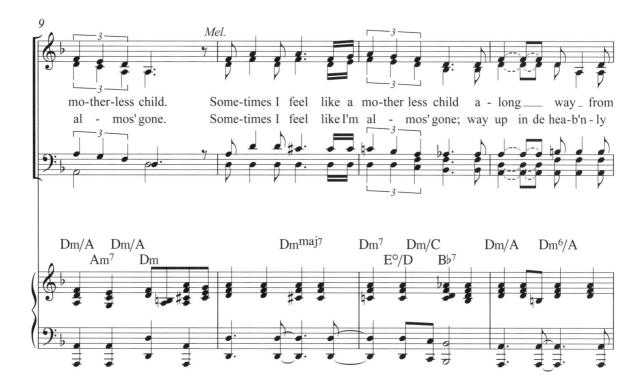

56 672

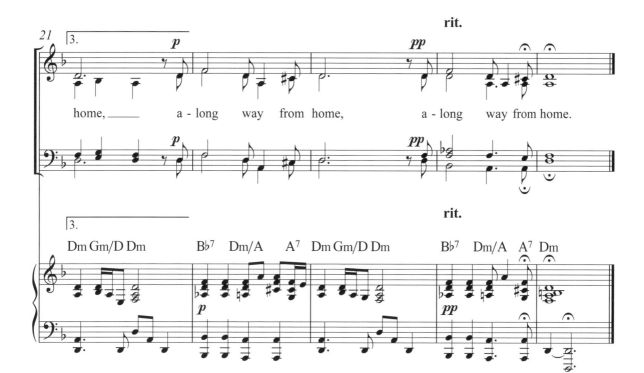

11. Holy, Holy, Holy, Lord God Almighty

Melodie: John B. Dykes (1823–1876)
Text: Reginald Heber (1783–1826)
Satz: Jochen Rieger (*1956)

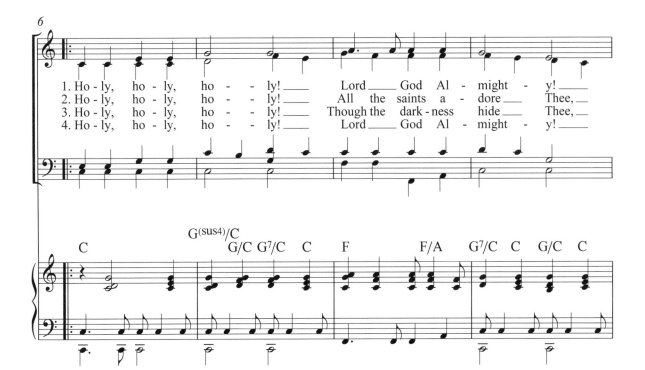

56 672

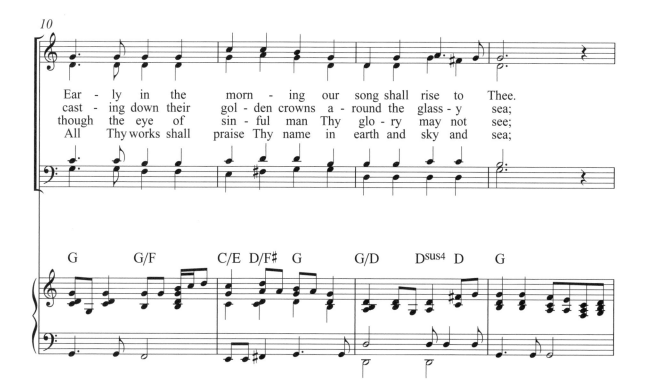

God in three per - sons, bless-ed Trin - i - ty.
which wert and art and ev - er - more shalt be.
per - fect in pow'r in love and pur - i - ty.
God in three per - sons, bless-ed Tri - nit - y!

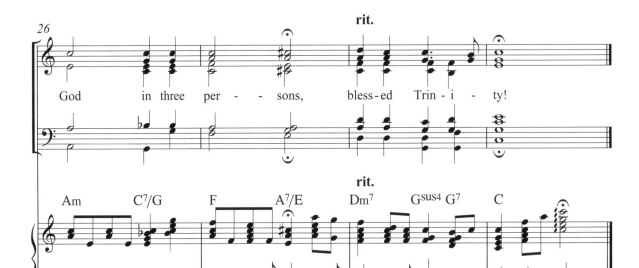

God in three per - sons, bless-ed Trin - i - ty!

12. A Mighty Fortress Is Our God

Ein feste Burg ist unser Gott

Melodie: Martin Luther (1483–1546)
Text: Martin Luther
Engl. Übersetzung: Frederick H. Hedge (1805–1890)
Satz: Jochen Rieger (*1956)

1. A might-y for - tress is __ our God, a bul - wark
(2. Did) we in our __ own strength con - fide, our striv - ing
(3. And) tho this world, with dev - ils filled, should threat-en
(4. That) word a - bove all earth - ly pow'rs, no thanks to

56

56 672

13. Holy God, We Praise Thy Name

Melodie: Wien 1774
Text: Ignaz Franz (1719–1790)
Engl. Übersetzung: Clarence A. Walworth (1820–1900)
Satz: Jochen Rieger (*1956)

56 672

12

Son,   ho - ly   Spi - rit: three   we   name Thee,

name;   Lord   of   all,   we   bow   be - fore Thee;
hymn   an - gel   choirs   a - bove   are   rais - ing;
Son,   ho - ly   Spi - rit: three   we   name Thee,

E   F#m/E   E   E/G#   A   A^maj7   E/B   F#m/B

17

though in __ es - sence on - ly __ one;   Un - di - vid - ed __

All   on   earth __ Thy scep - ter claim, __ all   in heav - en a -
Cher - u - bim __ and ser - a - phim,   in   un - ceas - ing
though   in   es - sence on - ly   one; __ Un - di - vid - ed

E   C#m7   F#m/A E/B A^6/B A/E E   E/D# C#m7 B/C# C#m7

14. Joyful, Joyful, We Adore Thee

Melodie: Ludwig van Beethoven (1770–1827)
Text: Henry van Dyke (1852–1933)
Satz: Jochen Rieger (*1956)

56 672

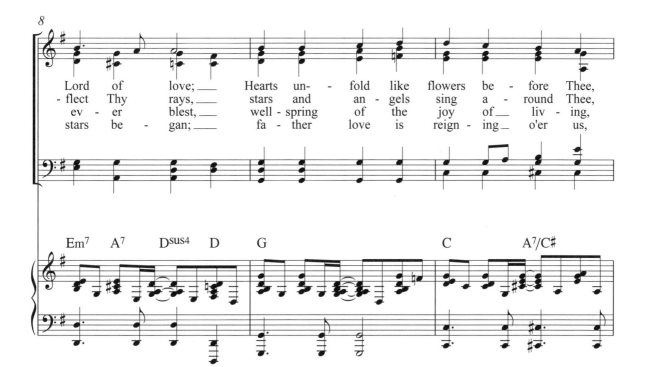

Lord of love; __ Hearts un- -fold like flowers be - fore Thee,
-flect Thy rays, __ stars and an - gels sing a - round Thee,
ev - er blest, __ well-spring of the joy of __ liv- ing,
stars be- gan; __ fa- ther love is reign- ing __ o'er us,

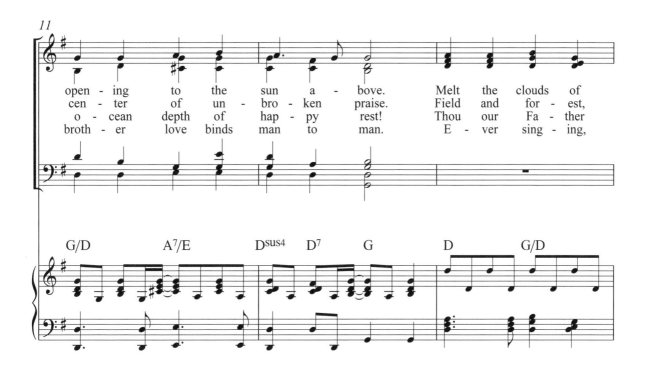

open - ing to the sun a - bove. Melt the clouds of
cen- ter of un - bro- ken praise. Field and for - est,
o- cean depth of hap- py rest! Thou our Fa - ther
broth- er love binds man to man. E - ver sing- ing,

15. Abide With Me!

Melodie: William H. Monk (1829–1889)
Text: Henry F. Lyte (1793–1847)
Satz: Jochen Rieger (*1956)

56 672

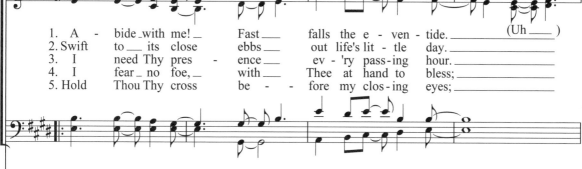

1. A - bide with me! Fast falls the e - ven - tide. (Uh)
2. Swift to its close ebbs out life's lit - tle day.
3. I need Thy pres - ence ev - 'ry pass - ing hour.
4. I fear no foe, with Thee at hand to bless;
5. Hold Thou Thy cross be - fore my clos - ing eyes;

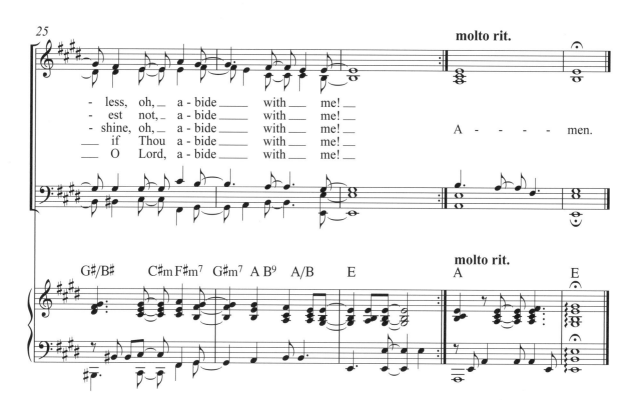

Schott Music, Mainz 65 672